Floods of Tears, Floods of Laughter

About the Editors

Gez Walsh burst on to the poetry scene in 1997 with his ground-breaking collection of children's poetry, originally written to stimulate his dyslexic son to read, *The Spot on My Bum*. Since then he has gone on to publish a further eight books of "Potty Poetry" for kids (of all ages) and regularly visits schools in the UK and abroad to perform his work, inspire  kids to write, and lead them in workshops and exercises to teach them that literacy and poetry can be fun.

He has also written four books in the *Twisted Minds* series of horror stories, the most recent of which, *Death's Door*, appeared in 2015. This year he is working on a book of his own poems for adults (for a change) and also a cookery book based on the recipes handed down in his family by his Italian grandmother. He became the official Poet Laureate of Calderdale in 2014.

Joel Duncan is a bright new talent who has been making a meteoric rise to become a regular performer at poetry venues in West Yorkshire and beyond. He was the winner of a contest in 2014 to discover and appoint a Young Persons' Poet Laureate for Calderdale, under the mentoring of Gez Walsh, and his  first collection of poems, *My Last Everything*, appeared in October 2015, including being named in the roundup of books of the year in the *Yorkshire Post*.

Joel is also an advocate for the place of poetry in education, pointing out with considerable justification the difference that poetry and writing has made to his own life.

Floods of Tears, Floods of Laughter

Poems and prose by the young people
affected by the Boxing Day floods, 2015
in the Calder Valley

Edited by

Gez Walsh and Joel Duncan

THE KING'S ENGLAND PRESS

2016

ISBN 978-1-909548-67-1
FLOODS OF TEARS, FLOODS OF LAUGHTER
is typeset in
Book Antiqua, Gentium Book Basic, and Gill Sans
and published by
The King's England Press
111 Meltham Road
Lockwood
HUDDERSFIELD
West Riding of Yorkshire

Printed and bound in Great Britain by
Lulu Press
Digital Print on Demand

Dedication & Acknowledgements:

This book is dedicated to the indomitable nature of the Yorkshire spirit, fuelled by tea, grit, and stubbornness*

*Phrase coined by Hebden Bridge artist Heather Dyrlaga, and you can buy a teatowel with it on in aid of the floods fund from her at bearfollowscat.com

Thank You!

Both Joel and I would like to thank all the students who contributed to this book, as without them this project could not have happened.

Thank you also to Kings England Press for going beyond the call of duty to produce the artwork for this book.

A big thank you goes to all the teachers of Calderdale that helped their students to take part in this project. Teachers are always the unsung heroes (and heroines) of our communities. They're often there not only teach the young, but also to help them to make sense of their environment and the world they encounter around them.

Finally a big "thank you" to you, the reader, for taking the time to buy this book. By doing so you have helped in no small way to help a community to rebuild again.

Publisher's note

Publishers don't normally write notes in the books they publish, well, not since the middle ages anyway, when a monk might have scribbled in the margin of the manuscript he was copying, that his cell was cold and his candle had just gone out, but in editing these poems I felt I had to comment on the technical standard of the writing.

The main reason why the editors decided to put all the entries into the book was purely and simply the technical excellence of the contributions. Many of them use poetic techniques and stylistic devices far in advance of what might be expected of someone of their years. Either they have been taught these things by their teachers, such as enjambment, assonance, para-rhyme, form, structure and personification, in which case it is also a testament to the excellence of their education, or they are using them instinctively. Either way, it bodes very well for a new generation of writers springing from the valley that produced Ted Hughes.

However high the waters might rise (and we all sincerely hope they are kept under control from now on) they will not stifle the creativity and excellence of the authors of these poems.

STEVE RUDD
The King's England Press

Note: Names of contributors are as they appear on the poems, exactly as given. Where a contributor's age is given, that has also been added. Where a poem was submitted untitled, the first line of the poem has also been used as the title. A small number of the original entries were accompanied by artwork or photographs which, for a variety of technical and copyright reasons, it has not been possible to reproduce in the book.

Forewords

On Boxing day 2015, as families in the Calder valley settled down to what should have been a day of feasting and happiness, the skies above darkened and then released a torrent of water so dense and powerful that those that encountered it will never forget it. The result of the downpour was a flood that destroyed houses, businesses, and schools, and washed away bridges and the basic infrastructure of the valley. The people of the Calder valley were only just getting over the previous flood that they had suffered only a few years earlier, so their misery was compounded, knowing just what to expect, having to start over again.

Much has been said, quite rightly, about the economic misery caused by such a disaster, but what about the emotional damage that such an event inflicts on the victims? What about the day to day living? Coming to terms with everything you own being, literally, washed away, in one fell swoop.

This book has been written by the young people of Calder valley, and it is a chance to see the disaster from a different prospective, through the eyes of the young. Don't think this book is a school project, though. It is eloquent, thought-provoking and helps both the reader and author to try to make sense of what happened on that fateful day, to make sense of the disaster, and to come to terms with the aftermath.

This book is not only giving young people a chance to have their voice heard, but also all the profits from its sale after print costs have been met will go directly to the flood appeal to help people who were affected by the disaster to rebuild their lives.

Both Joel Duncan, who is Calderdale's young persons' poet laureate, and I have visited schools to try to help to get young people involved with this project but the whole work is written by the students of Calder valley.

Gez Walsh.

The children who wrote these wonderful pieces will be our future generation. They will tell their stories of how the floods changed their lives. When all this pain and devastation has been washed away, they might dig out this book and find their names just so they can remember. It's always hard to recall what you felt as a child. When we get older we tend to exaggerate our stories and in time we start to believe that's how it happened. Our perspective on an event alters the way we look and feel about it every time we watch them unfold in our memories. There was some children that were excited by the floods, a few of the young writers took on the role of being the flood but everyone was affected by it in some way.

History is the product of people wanting to collect memories. We long to share those cherished moments that develop us as a person. Though we're more familiar with the devastation of the past, things that we either caused ourselves or couldn't avoid. So here we are, collecting the feelings of yesterday and freezing history in its place so the people of tomorrow will remember it like they were there.

Nobody really knows if the flooding has ended or this was just a warning. It begs the question if we are the victims here or is this tragedy a retaliation of mother nature? We never expected global warming to affect us this quickly. These poems sing a familiar song of our communities coming together. The rain took everything from us except from what it means to be human and the children have breathed life into that idea. I think there's a clear message that keeps afloat in all these pieces which is love and it will take a lot more than water to tear it down. This collection sends waves of mixed emotions throughout your body. It's powerful yet intimate, and an essential piece of history you won't want to throw away.

Joel Duncan

My Flood Poem

Silent slow and sudden the water seeped into the lonely lost
school which was once full of happy children.
Nobody could cope
Floating on top of the water the Land Rover wondered if this was
the last time he would be seen.
Nobody could cope
The emerald grass was covered by a swamp of mucky water.
Nobody could cope
Mountains of debris was piled up waiting to go.
Nobody could cope
Nobody
But we will be back soon.

Callum Ingham, Burnley Road Academy

Flood Poem

Rubbish all over the gardens
The town is like a massive swimming pool
People helped us
The Land Rover is abandoned
The once beautiful Co-op was half sunken
People helped us
The water is attacking Burnley Road Academy
The memories of Christmas have faded
People helped us
The devastation was all over the town
People helped us
They helped.

Tristain Nelson, Burnley Road Academy

What's Happened?

Standing up now for the school and the businesses trying find the rest!
It was there!
But not anymore!
Do you care?
Land Rover sitting there, someone trapped about to disappear out this world
Tears running down my face. I can't bear to look
Can't smile, can't laugh, can't be happy
I wish I could help to stop this.
I would do anything, I just want to help.
Different communities come to help
Memories of Christmas fading away.
I want to yelp
We will work as a team, it's okay
Everyone, everything gone
Our lovely world, our lovely village
Gone
Gone forever.
Just remember we're here.

Daisy Stuart, Burnley Road Academy

Flood Poem

Christmas is over, Boxing Day comes. The rain is pounding down like a band of drums.

Burnley Road, Riverside, Central Street too. They've all been affected, including you.

Dirt and sewage, the towns were smeared. You've been boated away, sad and feared.

Villagers and town folk did what they could. They did their big clean up, they took away the mud.

2016 comes, people are still trying. Families and workers can't stop crying.

Thank you Mythomroyd, Hebden too. We'll be forever grateful. Thank you.

Ruby Foulger, Burnley Road Academy

Flood Poem

While destroying, dragging and dismantling things, the water slowly submerged the suffering shop.
The murky water covered the once shining emerald green bushes, surrounding them in debris.
People looking around, trapped, trying to escape, waiting for help.
Would it ever come?
With waves rushing rapidly, the water spread.
Even the Christmas decorations tried to escape.
Looking down in astonishment
people stared at their village with sorrow.
Once loved toys lay there in amazement,

wondering how they ended up here.

Sofas sitting silently, stacked up yet unloved, unwanted.
Debris spewed out of doors, it was garbage not yet put in the bin.

Charlie Myers, Burnley Road Academy

The Reality of the Flood

Rising, rising, the waters rising, rising
Up the road.
People fleeing their houses
Seeing the reality of the flood.

Christmas is ruined, Christmas is ruined.
All the presents are soaked
Children crying, adults yelling
"Why us, why now?"

Now you know the reality of the flood.

Jake Wood, Aged 10, Scout Road Academy

Flood Poem

Like a bomb, the garden was destroyed
Why did this have to happen?
The flood is another canal
Why another dirty canal?
I stood there thinking this is not fair
Why couldn't it have been sunny?
Useless and abandoned, the Christmas light stood tall and proud
but with no power
Why, when it's Christmas?
Mountains of litter and furniture, damp and wet, once was loved
Why homes? Why toys?
Once was a happy village, shops were open, fun things happening
and now it is dark, dull and gloomy, shops are closed and mud
everywhere!

Why this little village?
Once was a road with cars and people on, now we see it as a
swimming pool
Why has this happened?
The woman looked down from the window, her heart suddenly
sank.
Why Mytholmroyd?
Why?

Holly Brooks, Burnley Road Academy

Flood Poem

The water attacked the innocent buildings
The water sneaked into people's homes like a burglar
Why after Christmas day?
The muddy polluted water flooded the gardens
Like rubbish, precious belongings lay there not to be loved again
Why after Christmas day?
Brand new shiny presents washed away
The road was like a sea
Why after Christmas day?
Why?

Jennifer Robinson, Burnley Road Academy

Flood Poem

The emerald grass immediately got invaded with water and ended up with a muddy, disgusting, freezing paddling pool.

Horrifically, cars got sunk like quicksand into the water with only seconds to spare.

Why is this?

Rapidly, the water speedily sprints into the bungalow with just one hope, that it will dry out.

Hopelessly, the lady looks over the balcony with horror and devastation.

Why is this?

With loads of crushed debris and litter thrown in the pile, it grew bigger as the day passes.

Meandering through , Calderdale became the lost city of Atlantis.

Why is this?

Thomas Clayton, Burnley Road Academy

Mytholmroyd Flood Poem

Mytholmroyd once a peaceful town now like a swimming pool
The Christmas spirit all washed away
Why did this happen now? Why after Christmas?
All you could see was murky, brown and mushy sewage; the poor
people, what they must be thinking?
Once sparkling emerald grass now a muddy and gooey mess
The town destroyed waiting for help and a sight of hope
Damage which you just can't describe
Precious things to people now gone for good
The village which so many people rely on obliterated

One of the worst floods ever in history
So many lives destroyed by this one flood which was terrible
Why Mytholmroyd?
Why us?

Thomas Hanrahan, Burnley Road Academy

Boxing Day Floods

Christmas has ended
Boxing Day comes
The rain is pounding
Like a band of drums
The town is dark, damp and deserted
It was under tons of water
Everything, everyone was helpless
The houses were being slaughtered
Burnley road, Riverside Central street too
The water is not clean
There is floating poo!
No one could do nothing but stand by

Everyone had to watch everything die

It was a serious matter, not a joke
The river rose higher, there was no hope
The next day everybody began the clean up
Everything was dirty and the walls were bare
No one went out, no one dared
Everything is starting to get better
Now that everything is clean
Most things are back to normal but all the Christmas joy is never to be seen.

Chloe Hoyle, Burnley Road Academy

Help!

Water everywhere.
Loss bound
Everything hit the ground.
"Why, oh why?" families shout.
Broken hearts in confusion.

Water everywhere.
Loss bound
Everything hit the ground.
People started to help.
This Christmas will be memorised.
HELP!

Isabelle Cox, Aged 9, Scout Road Academy

The Mytholmroyd Flood

Laying there unwanted, unloved, unneeded, the rubbish was
deeply saddened.
Looking down feeling distraught the lady looked at the
devastated village.
Why here?
Yellow sandbags lay helpless against the tidal wave.
Floating in the filthy water the maroon Land Rover nearly served
as a deathbed for a poor old man.
Why here?
Debris lay there never to be used again.
Why here?
Why?

Joseph Brooke, Burnley Road Academy

The Dark Side

In the middle of the night
The river rose high.
The boats won't float –
They were on the bank side.
They were stuck in the mud
As firm as a duck on the bank side.

The houses were, too.
Don't forget about the ruin.
Battered, they were,
Evicted too -

Mytholmroyd and Cragg Vale to West Yorkshire was flooded
And nobody will forget that dreadful night.
Right on the bank side.

Finn Sierevogel, Aged 10, Scout Road Academy

Pita Pata, Pita Pata

Pita pata, pita pata
God was having a big wee
While my mum was drinking a cuppa tea.

The water came from the hills
The fish were swimming with their gills.

After it was finished, everything was ruined,
Places wrecked,
Buildings were very wet.

Then that was finished,
It was over.

Isaac Tupling, Scout Road Academy

Flooding Mania

Everybody's panicking,
They don't know what to do,
The schools have all been damaged,
There has been a landslide, too.

The flood is wreaking havoc
And there's nothing we can do
Apart from clean up when we can.

Carmel West, Aged 10, Scout Road Academy

The Gods Had A Wee

The gods had a wee,
I bet you can see.
Now Mytholmroyd buildings are underground.
It looked funny to me,

But it's not people's cup of tea
Because their house has fallen down.

People started to show off and drove all the way off,
But got stuck before reaching the town.
A crowd of people shouted like a ram,
As moody as my gran.
They were like a distressed lamb.

The gods had a wee,
I bet you can see.
I guess you can't give Him the blame,
Because he flushed the chain!

Luca Lazzari-Williams, Aged 10, Scout Road Academy

Dread The Floods!

Too much rain,
The canal overflows,
The river bank destroyed.
Trees have fallen down,
Yet to be cleaned up.
Homes are destroyed.

But Burnley Road was the worst,
Landslide on Scout Road.
So now we are at the Ark.

Trees have fallen down.
Old people's homes are destroyed.
Marvellous businesses are destroyed.
Pretty shops destroyed.

It's raining again and again.
It's raining again and again.

It's pouring down,
It's pouring down,
It's raining again and again.

Phoebe Verry, Aged 10, Scout Road Academy

Flood Poem

The flood alarm is screaming
Everything is disappearing.
Stop what you're doing,
Because it's raining.

Water is rising.
It's so mesmerising.
Shops destroyed,
Houses ruined.

The flood has stopped,
Everybody's shocked.
Everybody is cleaning
Because nothing is open.
Covered to the top with mud and dirt.
Wellies and gloves.

It's all cleared up!
It's back to normal!
Hurray! they say.

Ruby Fisher, Aged 10, Scout Road Academy

Flood Poem

Heart beating
Waters flowing
Getting close

The water's coming in!
Oh, no!
The road's an ocean
Cool but deadly
Oh!

Look at it go!
Oh, no!
Water's rising,
So fast,
Oh!

Lydia Morgan, Aged 9, Scout Road Academy

Flooding Frenzy!

The rain started pouring
The river was rising, it was surprising.
Water rushed over the sides
And into the building, all over.

Families helped to clear out the houses,
The flood pulled people together.

The power line cut,
The road cracked,
And the land slipped.

The presents disappeared and vanished.

The cars drowned in seconds.
A shop got ripped apart.

Everything was trapped under water.
Schools got bashed to bits.
Mytholmroyd was no longer ...

Georgia Topham, Aged 10, Scout Road Academy

Flood Poem

Flood is screaming,
People are cheering.
Rain, rain.

It is pouring,
Now it is boring.
Rain, rain.

Stop your plumbing,
It is flooding.
Rain, rain.

Sirens start,
It's the screaming of your heart.
Rain, rain.

Rocks fall down
The hilly ground.
Rain, rain.

I look downstairs.
Where is my house?
Where? Where?

The tables have gone,
So has my pond.

Rain, rain.

Now I see the trees
In the winter breeze.
Rain, rain.

The flood has stopped.
Now it's dropped.
Rain, rain.

I feel so sad.
What a winter we have had!
Rain, rain.

So come on down
And help your town.
Rain, rain.

Abbie Simcock, Aged 11, Scout Road Academy

The Mytholmroyd Flood

The flood, the flood, all the evacuations.
All the dirty sand in the streets, left over.
The flood is like a scruffy, dirty beach.

Landslides causing,
Rain is falling,
What are we going to do?

Boxing Day, lots of hay
Lying in the dirty old street.
No more presents,
No more heaven.
What are we going to do?

Kai Fenton, Aged 10, Scout Road Academy

Flood Sirens, 7 a.m.

Flood sirens, 7 a.m.
Yet again, lots of mayhem.
Like the war, all over again.
Like we have to say goodbye to men.

The water quickly rising,
This is all very mesmerising.
"Quick! Clear the rooms!"
"Save the food!"

Water crashing down, over the wall.
Our back gate ready to fall.
Broken cellar window. CRASH!
Broken cellar door. THRASH!

The whole house is shaking.
What a mess this is making.

Isabella Stokes, Aged 11, Scout Road Academy

Mytholmroyd Floods

Mytholmroyd floods,
You're horrible.
They destroyed our village,
Helped the baddies.

Oh, so sad.
Luxurious houses destroyed.

Mushed-up mud left behind,
Raging water coming down.

OMG, more is coming!
Yo! it's flooding.

Dogs are drowning,
Food lost,
Lots of shops destroyed.

Oh, help!
Oh, help!
Don't stop helping,
Start helping.

Florence Winder, Aged 8, Scout Road Academy

Flood Poem

The river is high,
The rain is still falling,
People in bed.
Up and up it went,
The water still rising over the top
Into shops and houses.
People need to wake up soon.

Daisy Le Pla, Aged 9, Scout Road Academy

There's Something Happening...

There's something happening – it's bad, it's torture,
For out in the darkness all you see is water.
People sad and children crying,
Flooded shops and Christmas dying.
Now it's rushing down my street –
Oh no! It's almost at my feet...

Evie Guha, Aged 6, Hebden Royd Primary School

Early in the Morning

Early in the morning
I was tired and yawning.
My dad shouted me
For my bacon butty.

The flooding was rising and rising
Until it hit the horizon.
Pans floating around
Between the crowd.

Sainsbury's is flooded,
Tesco's is flooded.
Everywhere is flooded!

The bell is ringing
And the birds are singing.
The streets are flooding
And the plants are budding.

We need a digger!
The river gets faster.
"What a disaster!"

Max Creese, Aged 8, Scout Road Academy

Rain is Falling Very Loud

Rain is falling very loud,
There in Mytholmroyd there's a big crowd.
The flood is rising in people's homes,
While more is ruining their rooms.

They were locked in their houses,
Terrified and frightened,
The doors were locked
And very much tightened.

Rain starts falling
More and more.
While some of it
Ruined the store!

In the drain where the water had dropped
All the builders that clean Mytholmroyd houses
And they've seen wet trousers.

Some got flooded, some did not.
I didn't get flooded a lot ... not even at all.
I live a bit on a hill
Where it would stand still
And will survive.

Holly Andrews-Parry, Aged 9, Scout Road Academy

The Flood

The river is flowing and quickly growing.
I wonder when it will stop.

It got too high and burst its banks
And now we're out of stock.

Furniture floating, nobody's gloating
And everybody's vanished from sight.
People at the airport are ready for flight.

People are driving, they don't see the flood,
They all curl up in a bundle and fall in the mud.
Feet are sticking out of thick mud, black and dirty -
Nobody's flirty.

Slowly the sun comes out
And drives the flood back to where it came from.
So now we can clear up the mud.

Soaking wet sand bags slowing drying
On the rotting fence.

Help us clear up
And the street will sparkle
And be back to normal.
Let's celebrate!

Eve Dobson and Evita West, Scout Road Academy

What a Disaster!

The rivers are rising, faster and faster.
The houses are ruined, what a disaster!
The electricity's out, the water's about.
Stuck in our house, people about.

Our food is low, we might as well go.
Our sofa's afloat, where can we go?
It's a sky island of blue,
What can we do?
Our options are few.

The raindrops are falling,
They're having so much fun.
The place is appalling.
The raindrops are done.

What a disaster!

Jem Waite, Aged 8, Scout Road Academy

Flood Poem

Mytholmroyd floods, you're so smelly.
We never want to see you again.
The rivers were rising and the banks were bursting.
Everyone needs help, let's go and help.

Give them what they need, they're growing fast.
Quick, this Christmas might not last.
Get out of your houses as fast as you can.
The rain is coming very fast.
I definitely don't think this Christmas will last.

Amelia Watson and Martha Baldaro, Aged 9, Scout Road Academy

Mytholmroyd Floods

Mytholmroyd floods,
You should be ashamed.
The water has gone everywhere.
Holes are in the ground.
Oh, water is coming quickly.
Loads of people are worried.
More than enough water has come already.
Rain, rain, go away, come again another day.
Oh please, stop. Please stop!
You are naughty!
Do stop NOW!

Food is important but it clearly is not to you.
Loads of stuff is ruined.
Oh, so sad.
Oh, here you are again.
Do stop, do stop, please, please, please
Stop it NOW!

Matilda Baldaro, Aged 9, Scout Road Academy

Mytholmroyd Floods

Flooding is dreadful.
The river banks burst,
And then the water comes silently
Rushing into town.

The water is in the houses.
The people start panicking.
The rescue planes come.

But then the panicking stops,
But it is still not over.
There's tidying-up to be done.

It's time to move houses.
It's time to tidy up.
it was a dreadful day.

Tallulah Hirst, Aged 9, Scout Road Academy

Torrents of Water

There was a crash and a splash,
Rain came down,
A smash on the banks - walls fell down,
The torrents of wind,
Torrents of water,
Crash and a smash,
It all drowned.

Edward Lumb, Ryburn High School

My Dad's Work

On Boxing Day 2015, I woke up with a shock. There was water everywhere, it was like a river. I was extremely shocked! Who knew this could happen? It was terrible.

My dad's work got completely destroyed within just hours. Everything was in ruins, all of his cars, machinery, tools, paperwork, etc., were destroyed. For example, Peugeots, Citroen cars and vans. He lost everything.

His work was completely destroyed and ruined. Luckily nothing caught on fire or blew up. Kevin, the boss of the whole place, lost around £100,000 because he wasn't insured for flood damage. Also, he lost all of his wagons and cars. All of the power was gone for four days straight.

In Mytholmroyd, the power was gone for a long time. The water was seven foot high. A lot of KVA transformers were blowing up and making big huge bangs, as loud as a dinosaur roar. At Russell Deans there were mud marks on the door as high as three feet. White sands fell down to huge, sharp, harmful pieces. Minutes later, there was a landslide in Todmorden. There was lots of pieces of wood and metal, then cracks formed in the road. A lot of people were evacuated from their houses. A man around 70 years old had to have his sun-roof smashed so he could escape out of his Land Rover; the Land Rover was sinking and the water there was as deep as a Land Rover – in other words, a big car! Emergency services came in boats to save the man. Everyone is 100% delighted that the man had survived.

Todmorden Park was completely full to the brim with water. The roundabout was gone. You could not see a drop of it, as if it went into thin air. Also the zip-line, you could only see the top of it, everything else was gone. People were riding boats down the hill.

Emmie Calamatta, Aged 9, Castle Hill Primary

Rooftop Flight

"And you promise not to slope off to Tom's?" Mum, kitted up for a family gathering, was sternly addressing Danny, my big brother.

"Yes, Mum," he grumbled, avoiding eye contact.
"Well, I'll be off then – I've missed the cake cutting already. And this dratted rain will slow me down. "
The door slammed behind her. I counted under my breath: *one elephant, two elephants...* Before I'd even reached five, Danny got to his feet. "You don't mind if I pop to Tom's, do you? I won't be long." That would be his fifth broken promise this week, but I didn't really care. Michael Morpurgo's *Private Peaceful*, my best Christmas present, was waiting to be read. Danny shouldered his bag, and the door slammed for the second time that morning. I settled down for a good dose of guns, air raids and battles.

"Do you want to get your arse blown off, Peaceful?"
Suddenly a sound jerked me from my book. Was I dreaming? The air raid siren was sounding for the first time since World War Two. I ran to the window. There were soldiers on our street. Soldiers! The next thing I heard was a fist hitting wood. I hid under the bed, preparing for the World War Three I had seen with my own eyes.

By the time I realised, it was too late. The siren had not signalled an air raid, but a *flood*. I ran to the window and saw Mrs Carter from number 16 being helped through waist-high water by a soldier. I banged on the window but no-one heard. I was on my own.

I headed to the front door but stopped, gasping, half way down the stairs. The sofa was under water and my teddy, Vanilla, floated next to it. Still holding *Private Peaceful*, I grabbed my prized fountain pen from the stairs. There was only one option now: the roof.

I'd been up here before but not with a raging torrent below me. Tears streamed down my cheeks and my screams mingled with those of the wind. As I peered through the rain, I saw something coming towards me. Terrified, I was about to jump off the roof when something landed at my feet. I heard a soft coo. Now I knew what it was: one of Mr Stanton's homing pigeons. They used to be kept here and sometimes came back by mistake. Picking it up, I stroked its sodden feathers. "I shall name you Sapphire," I murmured.

I tore a page out of *Private Peaceful*, the only paper I had, and scribbled a message:

Help! 14, Stony Lane, Hebden Bridge.

Tearing a thread from my jumper, I tied the note to Sapphire's leg and picked her up, ruffling her feathers. With one tremendous push she was back in the sky where she belonged.

I watched Sapphire until she dipped out of sight over the horizon. My fate was in her hands. Now all I could do was wait.

Leela Guha, Aged 9, Hebden Royd Primary School

The Fierce Flood

I remember that day so clearly,
The sirens' scary sound.
The river running fast and wild,
And people all around

People at their windowsills,
Waiting for the help.
Wondering if that was me,
How I would have felt.

Standing in the rain there,
And seeing all the trash.
Watching as the helicopter,
Passes me so fast.

The roaring rain it hits my face,
I turn towards my home.
But not so many people now,
Have somewhere left to go.

I shed a small tear for them,
This really wasn't fair.
And everyone should lend a hand,
To the ones who need us there.

Robyn Edwards and Matilda Crisp, Castle Hill Primary

Eastwood

I live in Eastwood and my house got badly damaged by the flood water. The sewage water came in our house as well. Dad and Mum put the furniture on boxes so the water didn't get to the furniture.

When the flood water came in, it started to fill up the cellar. Then it came up through the floor and carpets in the living room and I started to cry. Then it came in the front room and all through the hallway. Dad asked me to go upstairs and we had to camp upstairs for about four days.

We had to tear up the carpets and the floor boards. The walls were damaged and the skirting boards were very wet, so we had to take them off the wall. So now we have to move next door with all of our belongings.

I got lots of presents on Christmas Day but because it was the day after, I can't even remember what I got and I haven't even played with them.

My wellington boots were soaked and very muddy. Everything on the ground was damaged.

The people next door have agreed to let us stay at their house for a bit, which is very kind of them. I am looking forward to going back home as soon as we can.

Freya Birch, Castle Hill Primary

When My Cellar Got Flooded

My house got flooded in the cellar and we lost all of our camping stuff. My Mum and Dad lost their wellies. It got all muddy and wet. It was about four feet tall and I was upstairs.

There was a frog living down the cellar but I don't know what happened to him.

The water came from three square holes in the cellar floor. My dad fell down one of those holes with his new trousers on. Next door's cellar kitchen got flooded as well and when they got all of the water out of their cellar, it filled up again from ours. It was a nightmare.

We went to my friend's house and we had to walk through noisy rain. There was water piping out from my cellar. The pipe came through the cellar window and onto the pavement. My dad was just in his pants because his trousers got wet from falling down the hole.

We have got two guinea pigs and they live outside. We thought we might put them in the cellar so they wouldn't get cold in the winter. But if we had, they would have been killed because the water was so deep.

My Mum and Dad went down the cellar with plastic bags on their shoes because their wellies were floating around in the water. They carried all of our things into the yard and hung them on the washing line. Then they put them on the pavements and the bin men came and took it all away, because it was dirty. Now we have to buy some more camping equipment before summer so we can go camping again.

Flooding can happen in lots of different ways. It can come up through the muddy ground, through the drains. It can come quickly down the hill, rushing towards town and can make the earth come off. The loose land falls into the dirty water at the bottom. This is called a landslide.

The rain falls into the river and the river fills up and overflows and the water goes through town and into people's houses, shops, pubs and churches.

When the canal filled up, boats got beached because the canal was so high. The water rises up when the barge is sitting on it and pushes it onto dry land.

People's vehicles and living plants got submerged. The water got higher and higher and things got under the water. It was like being under the sea.

People had to be helped, so that they wouldn't drown in the water, and people helped tidy up all of the mess. There was a lot to do. It might be still happening right now.

Our cellar is dry, but now there is a rat living down there. The rat had got in because the water made the ground all soft so he could squeeze through. I think the frog might come back when the rat runs away.

Margot Taylor, Castle Hill Primary

The Flow

From the first raindrop,
The tiny speck on the window pane.
The rain became nonstop
I didn't know I would feel so much pain.

The raging river,
Building higher and higher.
The unforeseen killer.
More devastating than an angry fire.

The rain beat grew louder,
Like a marching band.
The town started filling like a fish tank,
Bridges broken,
Houses ruined,
Unplanned.

Elijah Bottomley and Reece Turner, Ryburn High School

Floods of Tears, Floods of Laughter

Flying so high you can see anything that you had.
Love that feeling when the water's all gone.
Oversees to go to a different town to see how they're affected.
Of all the places it's our town.
Don't be mean, stay clean.
Super people are helping us recover.

Over fields
Farther on to London

Trying not to cry.
Ever felt like you can't stop crying?

All have been flooded.
Real homes have been affected.
Sorrow in the heart.

Floods can be so hurtful.
Low and high water rates.
On the car and in the house.
Over the roof, all in the water.
Don't be someone else because the floods have changed you.
Soggy food in the cupboards.

Over fields
Farther on to London

Like the coldness of the floods
All are sad.
Under the town, it's flooded.
Go to the Town Hall to live.
Happy when it's almost gone.
Try to explain when you're older.
Ever want this to happen again?
Real tears have shown.

Eve Whitham, Castle Hill Primary

The Floods

The floods are all mud and rain
They have caused some of us pain
We all need to help in this time of need
Forcing some to beg and plead
So we need you to help tidy up
And rid our town of the mud.
This is scary for some of us
This has been a tremendous flood
The theatre has been flooded out

That has caused some of us to shout
And some people can't go to work
Because all their offices are full of dirt
People are working hard to make things better
So fingers crossed it doesn't get wetter

Alfie Whitham, Castle Hill Primary

Floods

Rain, rain,
Blocks the drain,
It causes lots of pain.

Water, water,
Peeling off mortar,
It makes the walls much shorter.

Floods, floods,
Are the opposite of good,
As they leave lots of mud.
Mud, mud,
Washing away the wood,
By the big bad flood.

Dirt, dirt,
Is very hard work,
When it leaves lots of turf.

Leoni Brady and Ruby Marshall, Castle Hill Primary

Flood Story

My eyes opened, my mind was woolly, and I was still half-asleep. Stumbling, I made my way to the window. "What's that noise?" It was raining hard.

"It will pass." But my view of the canal forcibly changed my mind...

Why did this have to happen to us? We were just normal people, wanting to get on with everyday life. It was just nature; however the concept still seemed devastatingly unfair.

It sounded as if the trees outside had been ripped from the roots, as the sky darkened and rolled with thunder. "Wow." I didn't think that that situation could've got any worse, but with this oncoming storm - I just couldn't fool myself.

Opening the window, I looked on in sheer terror; the whole street was engulfed, before my eyes, in the murky, brown-blue water of the river...

Cautiously and carefully, I stepped forwards, into the repulsing, blue-brown torrent, feeling a cold, numbing sensation seeping through my boots and onto my feet. I would like to have said that I walked down the street, but that would have been an out and out lie because the road was fully submerged, producing the inevitable task, of walking with ease. Also, I was pushed by the gush of water so it was impossible to walk - or run - without being dragged by the water, at the very least.

The current was speeding up. The weir was in sight. Suddenly, without warning, my imagination grew wild; I think a lack of the internet for that day made my mind grow restless.

"No!" I whispered, picturing a hungry monster, beckoning me, *begging* me to edge closer, to be swallowed into the bottomless depths.

Falling into the weir, I needed to breathe. If I didn't I would drown - if I did, I would drown - there wasn't much hope of survival. But, there was still a slither of hope. I inhaled; joy ran through my very bones. My joy was put off quickly, as I bumped to the ground. What I saw, still amazes me to this day - a land, a desolate land - with no inhabitants (apart from one eel). I saw it; it saw me. We stared into each other's eyes. The eel slowly slithered towards me: its beetle black eyes dancing, scanning me from my toes to my head. Then, something haunting occurred; the eel, drawing breath, never took its eyes off of me, as it screamed, in a near-human voice: "WAKE UP! OH PLEASE DARLING, WAKE UP! WAKE UP!" My eyes were burning; I felt nauseous.

"She's waking! She's waking!" I heard a voice say. I opened my eyes. They were all there: paramedics, mountain rescue and my parents. A teardrop landed on my forehead. My mum was crying.

"It's ok, Mum." I turned; the canal and the river had joined forces, and were thrashing about the river banks. For a split second, a familiar black eel was dancing through the water.

I whispered: "Thank you."
Charlotte Holdsworth, aged 10,
Christ Church Primary School, Pellon

What's Happening?

What? What was happening? I was lost in a nightmare... my eyes were heavy, and a weird feeling brewed in my stomach.

"It's nothing," I told myself, "I'm hungry."

Little did I know I was lying to myself. It was a monster of a noise, a spine-chilling shriek that made my heart sink. Waiting was killing me; hiding wouldn't make things better. Just worse. Courage flooded my veins, I drew the curtains, and...

What I had just seen, was something only fairy tales provided. Opening the door, the green-turquoise water aligned my knees with its murky evil. As it harshly jolted me back, (when the sun was at its peak) the realisation dawned, the undertow gushed through the almost hinge-less door as it sloshed up the walls. Like a vacuum, it dragged the world around it into its grasp. Just then a cry from the room's corner stopped me in my tracks...

Craning my head 90 degrees amongst the rivulet that was once my kitchen, I stretched out, and reached for my cat. Directing him upstairs, I knew it was too late for me.

Silently drifting like a leaf in the wind, (which, considering I was racing through a very loud body of water seemed unreal), I peacefully let the water guide me...

Meanwhile, paces ahead, a weir lay, sniggering at the fact that I was practically asking him to eat me. Once the reality sunk in - sunk. Funny that. But the situation I was in wasn't. Bracing for impact I slipped through his jaws.

Drearily, my eyes adjusted to the new surroundings, a desolate land with seemingly no inhabitants. Golden sand traced the outline of my body like a glove to a hand. Upon the blistering heat (and loss of my phone) I naturally closed my eyes. The image my brain accepted was far from anything the real world could offer. I prayed the planet would take me to a familiar scene, because; I was nowhere that humans had been, and if they had, they hadn't made it out alive. I stayed motionless, pessimistically, wishing the world would swallow me. Again.

Despite the view my eyes rendered when the eyelids closed over them, the land was unprepossessing, and held virtually no promise. I had (for some reason) been summoned to a venue, almost purposeless. Would I ever get out?... or has the world already picked my fate?

"Hello," came a calm voice, "good to see you, son." I turned, and a tall male figure stood over me. "Dad?"

Benevolent eyes met my gaze. Sprinting round in a trauma-free mind-set I *tried* to hug him. A misty cloud of vapour arose to the air. "Please, take me home!" I begged. At those words, a strong hand clutched my ankle, and I disappeared among the sand ...

Repetitive beeps filled my brain. "Hon, are you ok? You hit your head," a frantic voice questioned. I looked around, to find I was tubed like a machine. "I'm fine, how's the cat?"

Jaiden Younis, Christ Church Primary School, Pellon

Blown Away

As I opened my eyes, and gazed out of the window, my eyes swelled with ice-cold tears. Was I in real life, or was this a nightmare? My head was spinning as if I had been beaten around by a raging monster, which pulled me away from the happiness of my wild imagination.

I looked outside the kitchen window again. The waves collided as one, and crashed against the softening surface, as if it were a great giant which was angrily rampaging towards its innocent victims. Life had been washed away, nothing but the sky-blue waves existed for miles. Where was Mom? Slowly, I paced towards the flooded door, and walked towards the weir: its gaping mouth pulling the water. I stroked my toe against the rough surface, my posture weakening. Angrily, wanting to get away, I attempted to release my foot several times, before I realised that I was being pulled into everlasting darkness.

Thump...Thump...THUMP!! I was partially conscious and was only aware of the jolt of pain that was effortlessly gliding through my weak body. I twisted and shook until I was sat uncomfortably and found myself surrounded by - not my nice warm bed - but a sky full of glinting stars, not a wooden floor - but a scaly like texture which rubbed against my bare feet. Where was I...?

I could barely breathe. I was being taken somewhere; but where? At that moment, I saw a large figure and began tracing the outline. I suddenly gasped... could it be? He left years ago. I looked closer, it was him. It was my ... my father!!! I was taken inches closer, before I saw a familiar face gloomily resting his eyes on my shaking hands. Your mother sent these last words: save our generation help the people.

"You see she died and left her power for you, there's no easy way to say this. Did you notice that she was angry yesterday? That was because she was controlling the weather - but this time, she was unable to stop it. In a way, when she drowned, it was because she felt obliged to do so. She thought it would stop the storm, but she was wrong, and now the wellbeing of all humanity lies in your hands.

Suddenly, there was a bang. I was on my own in what used to be my living room. I clenched my fists and closed my wanting eyes. That was when the flooding stopped. I stood there gazing longingly at a photo of my dead mother, I would never see my mother again. The floods outside may have stopped, but there was still another flood inside me, one that would only fade with the passing of painful time.

Sannah Janjua, Christ Church Primary School, Pellon.

Devastation

The muddy, Boxing Day floods caused devastation
to the nation.
The nation put aside their spare time to help those in
need.
The barriers broke loose and the reckless rapids came
gushing through; it was the day after Christmas, a day to
remember,
but not this December,
especially the mess it left after.
Sowerby Bridge to Hebden Bridge was pretty much
under water.
The victims cried out 'we need some help!' but the rain
kept coming down and turned their lives upside down.
People were using sand bags as handbags
because they had to take it if they
wanted to make it...

Zain Abbas, Ryburn High School

Tears Cause Floods. Laughter Stops Floods.

The water wasteland is upon us, submerging anything in
its path, growing time after time.
It's growing. It's coming.
It started with the parks,
Going for the football pitches
it was too much for the mud to absorb.

Lots of people rushing out of their homes to watch the
horror coming closer and closer. Nobody
could believe what was going on.
Then all of a sudden "CRASH!"

Something has fallen,
We have fallen
We looked down the road, we couldn't believe our eyes.

The contaminated water devoured the bridge; it was too
much...

We rushed inside to put our precious belongings
upstairs.
However, when we came downstairs it was too late.
The water was rushing in faster than Usain Bolt.
It was already too high: the fridge floating through the
house,
I hid upstairs like a little schoolgirl waiting for it to stop
thrashing in.

Suddenly, the plopping stopped.
It was over!
I waded downstairs. Hoping.
To my surprise my house, my house, it was demolished.
My house was no more.
I sank to my knees in tears.

Then all I could hear was laughter.
I thought to myself, why would anyone be laughing at this tragic moment? Why is no one crying?

I walked outside: family, friends and even strangers having a laugh helping Calderdale. Sweeping the mess, building flood defences.

Despite the flooding and the destruction everybody was having a laugh, making friends, helping others.
This disaster brought people together.
To make friends and become closer to loved ones.
So this is a disaster that caused people to come together.
Tears cause floods. Laughter stops floods!

Adam Clarke, Ryburn High School.

Crying Calder

The district of Calder with its beautiful looking valleys now like a gigantic swimming pool which nobody paid for.

The rain poured with all its rage all day whilst the rivers were hard at work growing stronger by the drop. Until the rivers let out like a tsunami. Then the sirens sound. In the pitch black was rage and upset. No power, people evacuating from the once nice, dry homes with their belongings, now a wet cold place.

The morning light revealed the destruction. Bridges had been torn from their place, roads now rivers. Sewers overflowing with all the waste left on the streets.

The football pitch was like a swimming pool with the top of the goal post calling for help.

Leon Parratt, Ryburn High School

Crying Calderdale

All at once it's broken.
Houses destroyed and the devastation on everyone's
faces; this was the day the rain came.
The downpour of the rain was never-ending,
it just kept pouring and overflowing into our streets,
with a rush, spill and gush.
This was the floods.

The swell of the water was dark and deep,
as horrid as a sorceress, gloomy, murky and dark in its
soul
This was the floods.

One by one we stood in hope.
Standing there, by the banks, hoping for a better day. We
wished the rain away.
People come together and everyone sticks like glue
because that's what communities do.

Buildings and roads are broken. Skate parks turned into
swimming pools. Cars became boats, and bridges became
logs, just floating in the flood.
After the flood had gone, it left broken emotions and
feelings of despair.
Shattered homes and broken dreams.
This is what happened on Boxing Day
by the Calderdale Way.

Abbie Dow, Ryburn High School.

Mixed Emotions

The river was high
But it was also low
Then Calderdale started flooding
Why? at first we didn't know,

Everybody came to help
Everybody used their free time
Although everything was demolished
At least we tried,

Dirty disgusting water
is running through our houses.
Early in the morning
So no-one would know

The water is getting high
I bet you wish that you could fly.
All that happened wasn't right.
at least we tried

Did we want the flood?
No
Did we need this flood?
No
But throughout this all, we had our
Hope.

After all the stress,
We made it!
all of this poem is to see
What Calderdale can be
and to show what we do as a team   :)

Joshua Rowlands, Ryburn High School

Floods Of Rain, Floods Of Laughter

Can the floods 2015 be the worst you have had?
When the water ran through your homes.
Businesses are horrendous! Why oh why do we get the
floods? Why oh why near Christmas?
Boxing Day was a downpour. When the water rose, our
hearts sank, we may have rain we may have snow.
Don't forget there will be an end.
Down pours - a bore they keep us awake.
Floods of Rain floods of laughter.
When the rain goes, we see the devastation: pretty little
Calderdale, Hebden, Mytholmroyd, Todmorden, Sowerby
Bridge.
Floods are there to keep us on our feet.
Teachers, pupils and randomers from far and wide come
to help the affected.
Hebden gets it all the time. Burst banks, Army here to
help.
Sandbagged roads help to build protection, bridges, cars,
nature floating
        away, away, away.
Aerial views from helicopters.

Ryan Parrish, Ryburn High School

Cry Me a River

As the rivers rise people begin to worry.
Geese splashed in the streets like children playing,
Birds bathed in the water like humans in the sea,
As cars drowned the army came to rescue.

The water began to rise and rapid rivers roared.
Above the trees and goalposts, creatures tried to keep
warm.
Sowerby Bridge, Hebden Bridge, Copley,

All flooded high.

Skate parks turn into swimming pools,
But with green, brown, contaminated water.
Businesses down the drain,
Faces turn from good to bad, the day after Christmas
day.

Memories were lost.
People saddened, but spirits of kindness,
Filled the districts to help those who lost,
Money was raised to help them get back on their feet
today.

Spirits of kindness helped those who lost the day after
Christmas day.

Lily McLean, Ryburn High School

Flooding Poem

The floods came with sudden rain,
Houses were destroyed and it caused lots of pain.

The cars, trains and people were stuck,
All the buildings... filled with muck.

The rain continued and the water level rose,
When will this end? Nobody knows.

Gladly, this time, no lives were lost,
However, all this came at a massive cost.

The government and services had to make a new plan,
Whilst all the people lived in a campervan.

Charles Parry, Ryburn High School

Devastation

Children and adults gather all around,
All the presents are underwater and nowhere to be
found.
Laughter tears have turned to sadness tears,
Disaster flooded in and people continue to have fears.
Everyone is trying to help their friend,
Really! When will this flooding end?
Devastation is all around,
As the flood waters swirl debris round and round.
Little by little the water drains away,
Each moment a painful reminder of Boxing Day.

Adam Cubbin, Ryburn High School

Floods of tears

F [floods ruining lives
L [leaving sadness everywhere
O [out of luck, out of laughter, out of love
O [outdoor area destroyed
D [destroying lives all over the valley
S [sobbing people everywhere

O [overflowing rivers
F [flowing all over

T [trying to escape
E [every house destroyed
A [amorous amount of water
R [reeking lives
S [sorrow spreading everywhere

Ebony Quick, Ryburn High School

How Would You Feel?

How would you feel to watch your home fall down?
And watch it happen all over the town.

For my house, there was no trace,
It's just the start of the devastation we had to face.

I just had to watch the gallons of rain,
That gave my village an unwanted fame.

It was just corruption and disaster,
That's what I witnessed a few moments after.

You can't even tell the buildings were there,
What have we done? It is not fair.

Everyone's belongings just washed away
All of it happened on just one day.

To this day, it makes my body go chilled,
But thank the Lord that no one was killed.

This catastrophe is one I will remember
On the 26th of December.

Eleanore Pell, Ryburn High School

No Hope

Swift stream runs,
Through the valley hills,
Weaving through proud trees,
Guarding Calder River.
Gentle raindrops fall,
Trickling into the stream.
Torrential rain hammers,
Pounding on the earth,
Feeding the stream's hunger.
Showing no mercy.
River flowing rapidly,
Demolishing everything in its path,
No hope now.
Everything submerged,
Under cold bitter water.
No hope.

Ella Whiteside-Smith, Ryburn High School

Boxing Day Devastations

Christmas was done,
presents were open.
Sitting, laughing, under the tree.
I looked out of the window
Such a sight I never did see.
Rain, rain lots of it and more,
a little I thought I can cope with
but this was a storm, a frightening sight
I went up to bed and hid from it.
Boxing Day, downstairs I came,
hoping the rain had stopped,
so imagine the shock when the newsreader said
"half of Calder Valley is blocked"

Blocked, I thought, what did that mean?
Then the image came into view,
my home town Sowerby,
just down the road,
there was a foot of water or two.
Trapped like animals, no chance to escape,
stuck in our house, bored, no fun
all I could do is watch the TV,
and think of those who were outdone.
Those who lost everything as the water rose higher,
chairs, beds, photos all gone
so when the water receded,
and the clean-up began
I thought that something had to be done.
But as I went down to help as New Year edged closer,
I was amazed by the sight that I saw
everyone was out with mops and brushes,
cleaning the streets and more.

Ellie Byrne, Ryburn High School

Floods

My home has grown overnight
I can go places I never thought was possible.
The roads, the houses, the parks and the city
Are all mine now! Freedom for me.
Captivity for everyone else.
Homes destroyed, but not mine
Mine got bigger and better
Their houses are useless.

Emily Rees, Ryburn High School

Floods of Tears

I think about it when I hear floods of tears because
people lost lives, homes and shops had to be shut down
to be redecorated.
I also feel sad when I think about it because I had a bad
experience on Boxing Day.
A day that everyone won't forget.
Most things in people's homes were ruined from the
floods.
I also think about floods of laughter when I think about
Boxing Day because even though I mostly had a bad day,
it turned out to be an amazing night because we had a
party that night.
I also saw someone that I hadn't seen in two years.
But I think Boxing Day was full of more sadness than
happiness because nobody could go anywhere and have
a good day because of the floods.

Ellie Walton, Ryburn High School

Torrent of Rivers

After a happy day as cheerful as a giddy child
Opening presents, to devastation of homes and gifts.
Happiness destroyed.
The burst of the banks.
The corpse of bridges
Lives distorted.
Cars drowning or on the river of dreams
As the hours went on, the help of thousands rescued the
trapped out of their water-flooded floors,
The helpers were as glorious as angels.
Thanks for all the helpers on Boxing Day devastation.

Joe Welsh, Ryburn High School

Floods Of Laughter, Floods Of Tears

The pallid faces of the people
How high can the rivers go?
Vanishing green to welcome brown
Birds flying high.

How pale they all went
Invading the space of the green fields
The changing colours from fresh to rotten
And the clouds floating above all our heads

The tears streaming down their face
Taking over like an army going to war, this is something
we won't forget
Like an apple changing over time
The blue instantly turned to grey,

And the screams on the inside that dread to be heard
Ruining people's lives and the pain is unforgiving
Fresh green to mouldy brown
And the rain began to fall

Oh the pain and the sorrow
Until the rivers of muck and dirt have gone down no one
will be happy
How unpredictable everything can be
The rain began to fall too hard

The rivers of pain
The rivers of sorrow
The rivers that will still be there tomorrow

Macy Mitchell, Ryburn High School

Everything Has Gone

Slowly, the outdoor swimming pools rise,
As the families and villages close their eyes.
CRASH! CRASH! CRASH!
People woke up one by one,
Realising everything has gone.

SPLASH, SPLASH it's up to my knees,
My house is filled with debris.
The town is in sorrow,
People are dreading tomorrow.
Everything has gone.

Nothing can be replaced,
Everything has gone to waste,
The town is now destroyed,
All of the citizens are annoyed,
Everything has gone.

Charlotte Parker, Ryburn High School

Floods of Emotion

Everyone was trapped on an unforgiving island.

The rain sounded like stones hitting the windows, cars, doors and even people.

Even though it was terrible, people were still smiling because they still had each other.

Whether friends, family or even complete strangers;

it gave them a chance to make new friends who they might never have met before.

Sowerby Bridge, Hebden Bridge, Halifax, Ripponden. Boxing Day was a downpour.

Lewis Ross, Ryburn High School

December Floods

Falling, falling in December,
Falling falling we all remember,

The floods of 2015,
The floods we all have seen,

A site yet to be cleaned,
Away from the awful scene,

Falling falling has all gone,
Let us all go have a quick British scone.

Rosie West, Ryburn High School

Rainbows Smiles in the Rain!

Falling fast beneath our feet,
Raising up beneath the trees,
Soldiers marching two by two,
This is a time we all shall rue,

The fields emerge with swimming pools,
The atmosphere is most certainly blue,
Animals astray nowhere to go,
Leaving us questioning,
Will this ever return low?

Days later some sun arrives,
And so reveals what was conceived,
A smiling rainbow shining away,
Glittering hope upon our hate

People gather all around,
Forming a community tall and proud,
Sweeping, swooping, gunk away,

Laughing together in the sunray,

Water drains lower and lower,
Fortunes revert, we stand like towers,
The sun beams bright shining away,
We all look up and shout hurray!

Moazzin Zaman, Ryburn High School

Flood

Down went the sun,
A gentle shimmer on the river,
A droplet fell to open the banks of a watery hell.

Dirty water, empty streets,
Towns getting flooded.
The rain came in rivers.
Flooding all the streets,
Trees and debris everywhere,
Up to my knees.

It eventually goes,
But leaves its mark.
Places destroyed,
Towns left in dark !

Kelsey Whitton, Ryburn High School

Grit

Damaging, upsetting, devastating flood.
Everyone wading through thick brown mud,
Shovelling and brushing the water away.
Families, friends - volunteering all day.
Rising over wellies, knees and chests too,
We've all been up since quarter past two.
And when the community all come out,
All hands together praying for a drought.

All lights out and candles lit
This is Yorkshire: home of true grit.

Max Hartley, Ryburn High School

Floods Of Tears

Rain, wind and terror!
The floods were as fierce as tigers.
It rained for days!
How many floods? It was insane.
People's spirits got more and more plain
 Not yet knowing that the floods will tame.
Even with the sky all clear,
 People still tremble with so much fear.
People helped the affected, even though they weren't
elected,
 With smiles on their faces they know there is no danger.

Tessa Holland, Ryburn High School

Floods Of Tears, Floods Of Happiness

Floods of tears
Caused many fears
In our happy little town.
The devastation caused
made our little town pause

Desperation.
Confusion.
And helplessness.
Just a few words to describe the utter devastation.

But throughout the huge downfall
Our little towns stood very tall
We proved to all
That even though we trip and fall,
We're all in this together!

The floods of laughter
Came pouring in after
as we took it in our stride
full of pride
our heads held high
our teamwork paid off
because we are Calderdale
and we will never fail

Emma McHugh, Ryburn High School

Tears Of Joy, Tears Of Sadness

The emotions floods bring are devastating
But the aftermath is something else, there are:
People sharing, caring, giving, receiving and giving a
helping hand.
Sharing something small can make a big difference to
someone's life
It could be making a cup of tea or making a person
dinner,
Lending someone clothes, anything can help when
people are in need.

The streets soon turned into rivers which filled every
side street.
You could not see the pathways, they were long
 gone down under
The deep dirty, dingy water.
The fields were drowned. You could not see any green
land.
The sky
Turned dark and grey then it began to rain again.

Laurie Oxley, Ryburn High School

Generous Hearts

Floods of laugher, floods of laughter
Fill the air to help and share.
Filled with happiness
Filled with joys
Community spirit with every little helps
Emotional exchanges giving and receiving
The Christmas spirit with floods of emotion
Generous hearts and kind spirits
Many hands made lighter work
People from near and far North, South, East and West

Floods of laughter brightens the day like a ray of golden
sunshine that warms a gloomy heart
People joined together one by one in small groups.
Children crying
Adults panicking
Elders miserable
All begging for a place to stay.
Many people are grateful, thankful and happy for all the
generous hearts.

Ellie Horsfield, Ryburn High School

Heart Broken

As the water rises at 6am,
The families are asleep.
The houses are destroyed,
Sowerby Bridge is ruined.
Heart Broken, Heart Broken.

The trees are drowning,
What can be to blame?
Sewage water running through the town,
Slowly making its own way through the streets.
Heart Broken, Heart Broken.

Everyone beginning to awake,
To this dreadful morning.
The water level is as tall as the Wainhouse Tower,
No one can stop it
Heart Broken, Heart Broken.

Phoebe Yousaf, Ryburn High School

Flood

It rose in a torrent of swirling debris,
collecting fragments of the lives of an entire village.
Tables, chairs, newspapers, beds;
the rich, the poor, the elderly, the young.
The water took no prisoners.

With it, it brought a sky the colour of danger
and a thunderstorm that smelt like the rainforest.
Grey thunder creased the sky and shook the
windowpanes of thousands,
sweeping the streets clean of people and leaving behind
a thick layer of silt,
as though just that morning, the world had been
repainted.

Together they came, emerging from kitchens
buried knee-deep in other people's belongings,
wellington boots and coats in hand.
An army of neighbours to scrub away
the remains of what had been the flood.

Anna Butterworth, Ryburn High School

Floods And Their Effects

There was always calm before the storm. It was Christmastime; the smell of roasting turkey and vegetables and the heavy scent of homemade mulled wine. Tucked up in bed, stuffed full with Christmas dinner, I could hear the rivers of rain pounding against my window.

The build-up was slow: first the river rose in height until the banks were no longer high enough to contain the torrent of water. Then the dedicated floodplains were overwhelmed with the volume of water that flushed down the valley towards the towns. It was a murky mixture of debris, fallen branches and the filthy white caravan that ran downstream.

Waking up startled from screams of despair, I stepped into the ocean that was my room. Everything was ruined; the magic of Christmas had vanished overnight and my home was all a colossal mass of destruction and devastation like the rest of my town, Hebden Bridge. I waded through the water until I found my mother. She was crying softly, clutching an album to her chest. "It's ruined!" she wept before pulling me into her arms. The warmth of my love didn't seem to aid my mother's ailment.

Rushing through Hebden Bridge, the water grew ever angrier at every stone building in its path, it dodged around corners sweeping away sandbags and saplings. The terror it rained down on the small town was terrible and tyrannical in its war of destruction. Nothing was left unharmed: canal boats toppled, bridges that had withstood centuries demolished, houses and businesses alike saw the full force of the water's anger.

I left my home with my family to stay with my granny and gramps away from the horror of the Boxing Day floods. They lived up a hill, out of harm's reach but had to travel everywhere on a little speedboat they owned. River, my sheltie, loved the abundance of water. He obviously didn't understand the risk of the disease-ridden water. He yowled for the chance to play, but every time my mother simply shook her head and told him "no," very sternly. Yet, he didn't stop, always desperate to play.

Gradually, the water drained away and cleaning projects could commence. Black bin liners stood proud like mock-castles, filled sky high with the ruined furniture, carpets, wallpaper or clothes of the citizens of this mighty town. Skips were also ordered and whole shop-windows were simply chucked away whilst the insurance men ran around anxiously assessing the damage in order to provide compensation for every store and home owner.

Weeks went by before I could even face going home; my mother still cried most days about the lost photo album which had recorded every significant and insignificant event that had taken place in my youth. When my family did return, I was shocked by the damage. My home was taped off with the unfamiliar yellow of biohazard tape and a typed note pinned to the gate;

Danger!

Baiba Antonova & Sammy Wolstenholme,
Ryburn High School

Destructive Downfall

The rain poured and poured
Storming down the streets
From door to door

The rivers rose
We all panicked...
The household froze.

Nothing seemed real at the time
I thought I was going to have to say goodbye.

The rain began to stop
All I could hear was drip drop
I looked around at what had happened
Shocked and scared I stood and stared

The destructive downfall scene
Seemed like a horrible dream

Lewis Stead and Cory Charlton, Ryburn High School

The Two Days

Christmas Day: everything was merry,
laughter and joy filled the air.
Children alert and dashing around,
there seemed to not be in the world, a care.

Boxing Day: there was a sudden change,
Almost like a monsoon, invading
our homes... our life.
A strong wave of rain began raiding.

I welcomed my loved ones,
Into my ornate house.
Devouring our dinner,
spending the last cherished moment, with my beloved
spouse.

At once everything was stolen,
as the water came gushing,
flood sirens warned us with piercing screams.
For us, the floods were crushing.

All our memories washed away,
because of the disaster on Boxing Day.

Emelia Marlor & Lauren Jackson, Ryburn High School

Falling

The water climbs as I fall.
I fall gently into the infinite darkness.
Tiny bubbles escape to safety,
And leave me behind.
The pain falls away.
The memory of me falls away.

The rain hammered on the rooftops and fell to the
ground;
The village began to float as I began to drown.
I should have taken their advice.
"Get out!" they called, but to no avail.
Stubborn, I stayed and refused to move;
A point, I was desperate to prove

 I lay here,
Cold and still.
Alone with my regrets.

Buried by dirt,

Blinded by darkness,

Broken by death.

Ben Nuttall and Emily Armitage, Ryburn High School

Overflow

I awoke. I had been dormant for years, but now I decided
to venture out of my banks. I crept slowly at first; no one
suspected such destruction. Days passed and rain kept
falling, giving me more and more power. Streets became
rivers, cars became boats and buildings became

reservoirs. I stopped everything in my path. The peaceful valley became engulfed in debris.

I didn't only travel through; I left behind broken bridges, failed power, collapsed history and crippled businesses. I flowed quickly through the streets, determined to create chaos. However, I tried with all my might to defeat the festive spirit; I failed. For days I persisted in this tiresome battle without success. I lost my final grasp of victory and retreated - for now.

Freya Clarke and Emmi Manning, Ryburn High School

The Floods And Their Effects

They were quiet at first,
But it wasn't long until everyone heard the roar,
The devastation seemed to appear in an instant,
The water crept up higher and higher, hour by hour,
The rivers burst their banks,
The town was submerged,
The raging currents even washed cars away,
And embankments were broken from surging water,

The victims took shelter wherever they could,
Leaving their loved ones to clean up the mud,
They left their homes and belongings behind,
There was nothing they could do,
Then the hard part came,
Reconstruction efforts were slow,
The community gathered to help in any way they could

Day by day steady progress was made,
Hopes and spirits began to reappear,
As people from across the country gave what they could,
Money was raised and supplies donated,

Time passed but the aftermath was still present,
People were still finding it hard to get over the terrible event,
Nothing will ever be the same,
We just hope this doesn't happen again.

Eleanor Coldwell and Hannah Greenwood,
Ryburn High School

Flood of '15

The river cascaded down by Tesco; accompanied by the flow of my infinite tears,
The more water that filled my boots, the more sorrow that rose in my body, causing me to shiver,
The time is yet to come that the rainwater will diminish and again my hope can be resurrected,
The cup full of change I had accumulated over the years washed away, taking all my hopes and dreams with it,
The bus stop, where I used to take refuge, had sunken into the depths of the abyss dragging my pride down with it,
The smell of stagnant water delved into my nostrils, inducing a nauseous sensation throughout my entire being,
As if being homeless wasn't ghastly enough, the enveloping gush made it hard to carry on.

Lydia Gordon, Harriet Adams and Leah Potts,
Ryburn High School

Water

The water battered the walls of its cell,
The clouds fuelled its escape.
Whilst growing; growing in strength.
Pushing the banks to the point of breaking.

The streets became swallowed by the river,
Shops were engulfed by the destruction,

Suddenly...

The town turned to darkness...
All power was gone,
Access was cut off from the once lively village,
Isolated from help; night time approached.

Hundreds of families
Had to brave the cold, hard night.

But hope was not lost...

Jack Tait and Josh Tetley, Ryburn High School

Devastation

The rain fell on Boxing Day,
Taking Christmas joy and cheer away.
Hundreds of shops and businesses down,
From Todmorden to Brighouse Town.

Sirens alarmed, the water was rising,
6ft under quicker than lightning.
Cars submerged, the towns in shock.
All within a few hours on the clock.

All of sudden, forced to leave,
Memories destroyed not a thing to retrieve.
Community Centres full and houses empty,
Not enough food to feed the plenty.

All occurred in just one day,
No more floods together we pray.

Jordan Cieciala & Beth Newsham, Ryburn High school

The Sowerby Bridge Flood

There once was a flood,
That brought no blood.
The flood was in the hood,
That brought lots of mud.
The mud was as thick as the air - a mud-bath.
The water was murky,
And the streets turned dirty.
The shops was destroyed,
People went unemployed.
Cars would crash,
The mud would splash.

Reagan Richardson, Ryburn High School

Flood Fear

Drip, drip, drip!

Something woke me that night. I felt the water trickling in. It rapidly rose until it was as high as my bed, it slowly enveloped my feet. A shiver ran through my body as I thought of how I was going to escape my own bedroom. The murky water surrounding me, it instantly began to climb the walls. The family photos were beginning to be swallowed up around me and I suddenly felt vulnerable.

I heard muffled shrieks from upstairs, alarming me as I made my way through the ocean of water which was now my living room. As I attempted to reach my children, the shallow sound of sirens were drowned out by the heavy rain, attacking the roof. My children embraced me in fear, after cautiously fighting through the water.

There was a sharp knock at the door, and several firefighters entered our now ruined home. They picked up my children in a sense of panic and evacuated us to safety. The relief of being on the boat was still not enough to stop me thinking about the damage that had already been done.

Kate Nicholls and Cora Barker, Ryburn High School

Fish Tank

Boxing Day had finally arrived,
And so had my Dad from the playground.
He woke me up with a smile on his face,
So glad that my Dad had survived.

But this was last year,
This time was different.
Why am I flooded in tears?
In my eyes there was fear.

Why does my house feel like a fish tank?
And why has my Mom turned into a fish?
I feel like I'm aboard the Titanic
At the end, when the ship sank.

I am literally brainwashed,
Running up to the deck.
There was no help in sight,
Suddenly I was lost.

The sea was filling my mind,
The nightmare is real.
Where is my Daddy?
I wish this could unwind.

Katie Illingworth and Shauna Hopkins,
Ryburn High School

The Sowerby Bridge Geese

Many call me a nuisance but in retrospect I have done no harm and committed no wrongs, so why do I deserve this? The destruction of my home, the mocking of my family during our struggle has led me to express my outrage and fight for goose-kind. I understand that humans too suffered loss during the Boxing Day floods but we did not make Facebook videos joking at their misery.

My gooselings have nightmares about the rising waters, the threat of death that they endured. We ran for our lives but even we could not outrun nature. While humans were devastated at the loss of their businesses, we lost one of our own. Jerry, my youngest with a bright future ahead, was swept away as the waters grew.

We were trapped; the fast-moving water gaining velocity. Gone was yesterday where we were safe, happy and frolicking with cars and causing traffic jams as we always enjoy to do. We love to waddle between the cars, head to the gym and get a quick snack from Tesco before returning home to our families. We were excited to play hide-and-seek, expecting an empty road as humans were still recovering from the festivities of Christmas, but imagine our horror when we awoke to heavy rain. We thought nothing of it and wrapped our gooselings in their woolly hats and scarves and began the journey to Sowerby Bridge. Anyway, I'm getting carried away... we were trapped and all we could do was try and survive.

Lillie Barstow and Meghan Chapman, Ryburn High School

Life Underwater

It destroyed everything in its path
The waves were like a kid playing in the bath
Homes, families, friends split apart
And so the water broke our hearts
Streets flooded waist-deep
Out of the window, people leap
Time stood still
The wind sent a chill
The rain kept falling.

It destroyed everything in its path
Lives weren't lost
But livelihoods were
Friendships were too
Life wasn't worth living
But after all the pain and suffering
Everyone came to help out
"It was climate change's fault!"
So why destroy our planet?
Truly it is our fault.
The rain kept falling

It destroyed everything in its path
But all together people were saved
Money was given to help
It will take forever to make our houses our homes
Buildings knocked down
The rain kept falling

And falling.

Adam Wolstenholme and Matthew Emmerson,
Ryburn High School

Devastation

Tiny droplets fell from the gradient sky,
Bouncing off the surface of my window.
Puddles gather in the cracks of the road,
Waves from under the tyres, cling to my skin.
Thunder erupts from the ferocious clouds,
Casting a shadow over the village.

Rapids; damaged furniture, a porcelain doll,
With cracks emerging through their broken frames.
Cars alarms echoed through the valley,
Along with the screeches of desperation.
Devastation crossed the ruins of a once unwavering
bridge.

Olivia James and Codie-Leigh Sparkes,
Ryburn High School

I Am A River...

I am a river,
I am strong,
I destroy,
I make people unhappy,
but I cause them to come together.

I grow stronger every time it rains, but I grow weak
when the sun comes out. I am unhappy, I destroy I ruin
people's lives.

I am the river and I run free

Blaithin Connell, Ryburn High School

Broken Boxing Day

Broken bricks told a story
Of a place where Boxing Day celebrations were made.
A place which drowned in the floods
Broken bricks are all that remains.

Broken hearts swimming through the streets
Of those who were, until that time celebrating the festive day.
A place where people's lives slowly floated away,
Broken hearts are all that remains.

If only I could've protected the town's history,
instead of it streaming away
If only I could go back to the time to warn my friends
About what was coming to wash our livelihoods away.

Your tears were like the flash floods;
Sudden and no warnings in sight but...
Your future is bright and sunny
With no more broken hearts or worry.

Olivia King and Farrah Chapman, Ryburn High School

In Our Town Of Sandbags

Waves submerge crying Calder,
While happiness is washed away,
Our streets are water wastelands,
As rapids clear alleyways,
In our town of sandbags.

Contaminated water drags,
While electric crocodiles drive,
As many put up a white flag,

And surrender to the British weather,
In our town of sandbags.

Forever we will remember,
Our washed away boxing day,
When love danced away the rain,
Away with our water December,
They all will say,
In our town of sandbags.

Beth Langan, Ryburn High School

Filled With Joy

Filled with joy
Lots of happiness
Out of worries
Out of your home
Dancing all around
Singing and dancing

Out of happiness
Flooded with joy

Lots of people
All laughing
Urge to start again
Gone away
Hugs all around
Tears of joy
Round again
Everybody happy
Full of damp
Lost everything
Out of money
Out of your house
Damp floors and walls

Soaked by the water

Out of jobs
Floods made you stronger

Tears flow
Everyone sad
All gone
Ripping of damp wall
Starting from scratch

Jake Tyson, Ryburn High School

Floods of Tears

It was 3:00pm -everything was fine. A few minutes later water started rising from the grate. The water had already flooded the field across from my house.

By the time it was 6:00pm the whole village had flooded and the water was rising up the front of my house.

By 11:00pm the water was at the top of my front step and slowly subsiding. The next morning all the water had gone and the terrace houses across the road from me were destroyed.

My dad's cars were totally wrecked and so was all the stuff in my garage. People brought free food for all the people helping clear people's houses.

Floods of tears... Floods of tears.

Maddy Pickles, Ryburn High School

Water Hits Calderdale

At 7am on boxing day
nobody dared to say hooray.
Heavy rain caused the waters levels to rise.
In the living room wet furniture lies.
The floods caused many tears
and revealed all the children's fears.
A man I know saw lots of water
chase after his young daughter.
I was scared for GW taxi rank,
which oh so very nearly sank.
Unfortunately we was left with a mess.
I couldn't help everyone but I did my best.
Many houses all around Calderdale
have signs outside saying up for sale.

Kieran Horner, Christ Church, Sowerby Bridge

Flood Woods

I could see the flood
rising in the wood.
Many were feeling sad
the damage was too bad to feel glad.
I remember Auntie Kim,
just standing still when the lights went dim.

It was a watery hell when the rain fell
because of the disgusting smell.
Rain will you stop, it's time to quit?
Now I'm scared when the clouds start to spit.

Maddison Johnson, Christ Church, Sowerby Bridge

Ferocious Floods

Floods as fierce as lions
Everyone's belongings gone
All roads like rivers
Overflowing the banks.
The rivers crying as fast as lightning.

We were inundated with help
As many were helped, some felt obliterated.
So many unfortunate people losing everything.
Sentimental values gone forever.
All the flood water scarring homes forever.

The water being low then rising higher and higher.

Outside there was a flood of tears.
The rivers were gushing with tonnes of water
All the people devastated, distraught, desolated
Thousands and thousands of people in shock

Muneebah Rakhman, Ryburn High School

Floods of Tears, Floods of Laughter

Floods of laughter when you win
Floods of tears when it all goes in the bin

Floods of tears when you dance
Floods of laughter when you have a chance

Floods of laughter on the stage
Floods of tears in the stage

Neve Furness, Ryburn High School

Floods of Tears

It all started on the 26th of December 2015. When all the devastation happened, people's houses and presents were ruined - the festive fun had ended.

You could hear people shouting for help and some were in floods of tears.

No-one knew where to go or what to do. There was water in the garden and everywhere.

There was no escape.

Natalya Mandidzidze, Ryburn High School

Not all was Bad

Our beloved Calderdale
Made us come to fear
An unexpected terror
Made us cry from within.

As it got worse and worse,
More of the community jumped in
And everything it took out
We all helped with a victory cheer.

When you ask the elderly,
They called this event an unexpected overflow
As the last one to happen
Was about 50 years ago.

By giving your hand
And giving your care
Our community
Is now free of what dared to get in.

Now all the families
That lived within

Are now crying
With happy tears
Not all was bad?!

Josh Evers, Ryburn High School

Obliterating Floods

As heart-breaking as possible,
When the rain towers down,
And causes an upsetting frown.
Drowns the photographic memories,
Of your friends and family.

The water that builds up upon us,
People deserted and trapped for
days and days on top.
Inhabiting destruction all around
The world.

On the other hand, we have supported
Our community with a special
Bond all around us.
The money we raised and the community
Spirit we had helping all the
Heartbroken and distraught families.

The causes of the devastating floods is major.
They are floating memories.
Many people were badly affected.
Even though there were bad things
That happened, the bright side is
It's brought our society together.

Codie Roper, Ryburn High School

On That Day

On that day
It rained and rained
On Christmas Day.
It rained and rained
On that day .

Boxing Day came
And still incessant rain!
But later that day,
the floods arrived

The water broke through
And greeted people.
Everyone ran for cover.
For safety.

All the memories
Pictures and items
Lost to the water

But people's spirits
We're not lost
Everybody helped
From London to Mytholmroyd

People cleaned streets,
 Houses and shops.
 Everyone started to
Cheer up a bit.

Our little town
is back now
Everyone is happy

But still people
remember about
what happened on that day!

Jake Teer, Ryburn High School

Floods of Tears

The vicious rain came flying down,
The strong winds came charging through Calderdale.
The long and thin river was growing rapidly.

Hebden Bridge was ruined,
Sowerby Bridge was flooded
Mytholmroyd was destroyed
Calderdale was dead!

It was like a horrifying ghost town
Empty, lonely, nobody, creepy.
Everything was ruined, everyone was sad,
It was a disaster.

Niall Tattersley, Ryburn High School

Floods of Tears Floods of laughter

Laughter is like a treasure chest
Sadness is a crazy mess
But when the water is clearing up
we all have to get a cup
to clean this all up

Trinity Baguley, Ryburn High School

Raging Water

Wickedly, I whacked the shop doors.
Pounding to get through, to flood their shops, and bring
devastation to the people and the town.
I saw people fleeing from their houses as quickly as they
could into boats outside.
I, the water, was raging!
The wind and the rain ploughed me into the cars and the
buildings.
I flooded the cars up to the top. The old bridge was
falling down in the weight of me.
The rain was stopping the wind was dying but I kept
going, powering through the town.
I was slowly going.
Dying!
It was painful; it hurt. I didn't want to go!
I wanted to cause more trouble, but they were stopping
me with sand bags and sweeping me in to the drains.
I was depleting, quickly disappearing
in to nothing.
They hated me! I don't know why the rain made me. I
didn't make myself.
Then when I came I just wanted to play, have fun, have a
joke.
But they didn't want me to play, they just wanted me
gone.

Marcus Rossi, Ryburn High School

The Day After Christmas

The day after Christmas
Everyone's joyful and happy.
It starts to rain heavily
But no one looks back.
Then it comes and hits everyone
Like a surprise attack!

The people cried out
"Oh when will this stop?"
But the rain kept coming
No matter what.

No one expected the floods.
No one wanted more.
The incessant rain ruined homes
And made everyone need help.

The floods created sadness.
The floods created tears.
But the next day came
And everything was clear.

Szymon Dziel, Ryburn High School

Raindrops

I wish it would end.
Why us?
Just after a happy event,
I just don't understand,
It was supposed to be grand.
Everyone is upset, their houses demolished.
It was like the water would never stop coming,
Like a waterfall moving onwards to somewhere else.

Someone help!
We have nowhere else to go,
The water is telling us no,
We cannot escape from this.
The water is coming,
We can see it in the distance.
It is coming,
Rushing at us.
It was like the water was running a race, eager to win.

I could smell the sewer,
The rotten nasty smell.
The water isn't fresh,
a murky-green colour!
Dogs and cats floating on things trying to get out.

In the end it all worked out,
Helping hands,
Getting the water away,
Boys, Girls, Men and Women helping each other out.

We now live in a happy neighbourhood,
It all ended.

Leah Woodyatt, Ryburn High School

Rising Rivers

It was a mind blowing experience. The rising rivers were terrifying. The colour of the brown water. Disappointed, horrified and devastated. The taste of sickness in the back of your throat.

The rain was so substantial and consistently heavy over quite a long period of time; it meant that the people who were affected had to work quickly to get all their belongings, family and pets upstairs to stay safe. Until the rain relented to enable assistance from the rescue people who came to take them from their houses to safety. The looks on their faces: pain and devastation.
You could see the water rising up above the height of the cars.

It was not only houses that were affected from the flooding, but also a lot of livelihoods and business.

The people who lived in the homes that were destroyed had to find somewhere else to live until their houses were cleared and cleaned. If they had continued living in their homes, then they may have picked up a disease because everything could well have been contaminated. They wouldn't be able to live in such a dramatically devastating situation that they were in.

Amy Barron, Ryburn High School

Floods of Tears, Floods of Laughter

Those broken bricks told a story

of a place where dreams were made.

A place which drowned in floods

those broken bricks are all that remains.

The funny memories told a story

Of a place where dreams were made.

A place covered in happiness

Those funny memories still remain.
Rosie Ransley, Ryburn High School

Sadness in December!

On Boxing Day last year,
Our towns were filled with fear.
The rain would not stop falling;
It really was appalling.

The flood defences gave in
And our houses and shops caved in!
There was nothing anyone could do
But watch and think boo-hoo.

The community pulled together.
The clean-up seemed like forever.

But nearly two months later
The towns are looking a lot greater.

The floods may have destroyed our homes,
But it couldn't destroy our spirits!
Some people can tell the tales
 While others unfortunately lived it.

Kacie Sutcliffe, Ryburn High School

Shaken But Not Stirred

Calderdale was hit by horrific floods that devastated
houses and businesses and ruined some people's
Christmas.
Dampening their New Year!
The water was high in Sowerby Bridge.
Flood defences were washed away as the raging torrents
tore through the towns.
 The rivers looked like fast flowing lakes.
Fire and rescue services were called out all through the
day as the rain fell and fell and rivers rose.
The water rose as high as some shops in Mytholmroyd
homes and businesses swamped.
The community spirit is amazing,
people making food and giving it to the people helping
clear up and the families whose homes have been
destroyed.

Isaac Burbidge, Ryburn High School

Smell The Dirt That Floods The Ground

The rain falls so hard
destroying the ground.
 Ripples in the water,
 People devastated,
as they watch the floods outside.

Buildings have collapsed.
People's lives have been destroyed:
Some have been made homeless,
As the rest worry about how to fix this mess.

People are worrying, saying "What do we do now?"
But all they can do is plead and help.
The inside of homes have been ruined.
They say to themselves "How can I afford to fix this right
now?"
But the community brings cheer
As everyone helps out
West Yorkshire will be back to normal soon,
leaving the history behind.

Millie Antemes, Ryburn High School

Day After Christmas

Day after Christmas
We all start to frown
News all around
Looking like a clown
With clouds filling up with rain
With pain
We all ride a cart
To be apart.

Tayla Kemp, Ryburn High School

Floods Of Tears, Floods Of Laughter

As the water rushes down the street,
Cars drowning under the water,
People coming to save the day,
As tears gush down their face,
Christmas fears, presents gone,
Water everywhere,
No place left to call home,
The waters all gone,
Christmas is over,
Finally at rest,
Houses destroyed,
Presents all gone,
The waters stopped flowing,
Happiness is coming,
No need to panic,
No need to worry.

Teyla Widdop, Ryburn High School

The Day After Christmas

The water rising into the valley,
The rain hammering to the ground
Making the river burst its banks
On the day after Christmas.

Water getting into people's homes
The angry water destroying everything in sight
Leaving people lifeless
On the day after Christmas

All the water from the rain sliding down the hill
Landing in the terrifying floods that filled the Calder
valley

All of the dirty sludge left behind
On the day after Christmas.

Connor Hardy, Ryburn High School

The Day After Christmas

On Christmas day we all went away,
But when we got back our house was collapsed.
Nothing left but wall and rubble.
Now our house a giant puddle.

The rain is getting worse,
The flood is rising.
The streets are empty but the houses are full,

The water won't stop, until the buildings drop.
We wait for help but no one is near.
The water won't stop, so
We all sit in fear.

The flood is reckless.
Destroying everything in its path
The rapids of pain
The floods of death
We all sit in fear.

Ryan Smorthit, Ryburn High School

Through The Window

Through the window, I can see raging rapids rolling towards me as it's demolishing anything in its path, from past and present.
Through the window, I can hear people crying no Christmas cheer: nothing but fear!
Through the window, I saw personal treasures floating past our door;
lifetime of memories gone forever more.
Though the window, I looked up and saw the help and rescue we pleaded for; they came by air. They came by foot. They came by car. they came by truck.
Though the window, I looked left and right to a barren place not so bright
No Christmas light for all to see, no festive joy for you and me!
Though the window, I can see people pulling each other to their feet, as the clean-up begins.
After the revolting floods, we all start to realise what the flood has done to us.
Through the window, I saw people bringing donations to our door: food, drinks, toys and more, wishing us luck for ever more.
Through the window I saw children playing with salvaged and donated toys which gave them lots of joy
Though the window, people queued as the church started to serve fresh food to people like you.
Though the window, as the clean-up ends people start to work again as businesses and homes get back to normal again
Through the window, young and old together.
Community spirit it lasts forever.

Josh Michael Gee, Ryburn High School

Today I Saw It Raining

Today I saw it raining,
Bashing the window pane.
The water was coming in the hallway and rushing down
the lane
I can hear the creaks and cracks from the roof trying to
break back.
I gather my things and leave with my family.
We don't know when we will return.
Soon, hopefully!

The rain is calm now,
The house seems empty somehow.
The floods got so high, there was barely enough room in
the sky.

The living room was like a battlefield
But after, there it was no poppy field!
The carpet is ruined and the walls are damp,
The clocks don't work and the couch is stagnant.
Tell me this is a nightmare and that it's all a lie.
Tell me that my house doesn't look like a pigsty.

Finally we have cleaned everything up,
The horrible hallway, the badly beaten bathroom and
even the battered bathtub!
The house is finally tidy and we are back to normal,
I could have done with a Christmas without all this
trouble.

Eleanor Wade, Ryburn High School

Together

Everywhere flooded,
Everything under water,
Everyone in shock.

The realities,
Tears flow down the river,
With lost furniture.

All lost and broken,
People crying in horror,
Devastation spreads.

Sadness to laughter,
Under twenty four hours,
The clean-up started.

People came to help,
From here, there, everywhere,
From the beginning.

Still cleaning up,
The floods were a big horror,
Still all together.

Alice Denham, Ryburn High School

Town of Sandbags

Tip, tap, tip, tap the rain's coming down,
It's early in the morning but still coming to town.
Halifax, Hebden and Sowerby Bridge,
Waters steadily rising to the top of your fridge.

The sirens are screeching,
It's starting to flood.
It's a town of sand bags,
Start waving the red flags.

"Oh no! The water's coming in!"
Families are starting to panic, they'll have to stay in the
inn.
"Help! Help! I'm stuck in my car!"
They pulled me from the sun roof next to the bar.

The sirens are screeching,
It's starting to flood.
It's a town of sand bags,
Start waving the red flags.

It's not just the roads and houses that were flooded,
It was also mammals and animals that are cold blooded.
However rivers and streams started to build,
And parks became swimming pools that started to be
filled.

The sirens are screeching,
It's starting to flood.
It's a town of sand bags,
Start waving the red flags.

One month later the floods are going away,

With the community spirit we'll be back to normal one day,
Because for everyone that came to help should be applaud.
But no one will ever forget the devastation that was caused,
The waters not laughing in our faces anymore.

The sirens aren't screeching,
It's no longer flooding.
It's not a town of sand bags,
Start waving the green flags.

Anya Wasilewski, Ryburn High School

Water Break

Tip, tap! Tip, tap went the water.
Houses breaking, people crying it was a slaughter.

Beep! Beep! Went the traffic.
Water rushes through it was horrific.

The debris sticks all over the floor
As wind rushes and rain pours.

People unaware of what's outside
The waves crash like a tide.

As the water flows a reflection from the sun
Ducks, fish and geese are all having fun

Bradley Justice, Ryburn High School

We Awoke That Morning

We awoke that morning with no noise,
I got dressed as usual, after all it was only Boxing Day,
The water neither running nor moving,
Still as can be.

We awoke that morning, not to what I expected,
The water was up to the centre of my house,
I opened my window to find I was only a metre away
from the water.

We awoke that morning our presents gone to waste,
Electrical goods broken away, why did the rain stay?
Our living room gone, our kitchen a mess,
This truly will be a Boxing Day we won't soon forget!

We awoke that morning people gathered from all over,
Helping every person with their homes,
Food, time, money and more raised for us,
The public we have learned to trust,
This truly brought us together,
Despite the awful rainy weather.

Mary Sulich, Ryburn High School

Flood Relief

As the water rushes
to the streets people
put their wellies on
their feet to rush
out to see the
devastation as
they lose their
reputation of being
brave as the tears gush
down their face
they are all losers
in this race.

Cameron Pegram, Ryburn High School

The Flood...

The water rushed down the streets, like a pupil trying to be first in the lunch queue. Crushing everything in its path, the deadly liquid oozed down the streets. Rapidly rushing, pelting rain like bullets.

The polluted plethora of dirty debris. The Land Rover submerged in a murky gloom of water. And of course, the destruction. The piles and piles of memories.
Once treasured.

Now, lost...
Cal Marsden. Burnley Road Academy

The Boxing Day floods

One lone man helping to cleanse the mess,
It is a water village,
A woman wondering why couldn't there be less,
A swampy marsh as a garden,
I thought god was supposed to bless,
A red and white land rover slowly sinking into a quick
sand like river,
The after effect devastated the whole village,
Nobody knew,
Furniture wasted like the food at Christmas,
Nobody knew,
The power of it was enough to destroy a building,
Nobody knew,
As if an ocean had gobbled up the whole village,
Nobody knew,
Once football field now an ocean,
Nobody knew,
Two lone goal posts stood there like staples in some
paper,
Now they know,
Now they do.

Anita Gosling, Burnley Road Academy Y6

Flood Poem

The polluted water took away all the excitement and
happy Christmas memories,
Happiness gone away,
Why now?
All the schools lonely and wrecked,
In the parks where the children play,
Why now?

People travelled from far away just to help us.
Did you thank them?
Hebden Bridge and Mytholmroyd is never going to be
the same.
Why did this happen?
This is a message from all of us.
We couldn't thank you more.
If we didn't have help from you, we wouldn't have got
this far.
You made us smile.
So thank you!
We appreciate it!

Shaneah Timewell, Burnley Road Academy

The Flood

The healthy green bushes stood
Proud with the murky brown water
Surrounding the bottom
There's too much
Cans, bottles, furniture, and muck
Was left behind from the terror and distraught
The red Land Rover getting
Pushed to its death
There's too much

The power of the weather
Blew down the
Shop
Shocked and scared the woman
Stared at the deadly
Water
There's too much
The shop, gas station, school and ground
Covered in a big blanket made of
Water
The Christmas spirit around
The place got washed away
There's too much
The poor man alone
Unblocked the drains but it was no use
The grass, the goal posts nearly all submerged
There's too much
Too much

Marcus Gurney, Burnley Road Academy

Flood Poem

Mytholmroyd's crumbling to pieces, the beautiful town,
gone, but what can be done?

The emerald debris is sinking, when's this nightmare
going to stop? they were thinking.

Little vulnerable man sat in his car, he didn't mean to go
this far, his life is at risk, we need some help quick; he
hasn't drowned, thank God!

They would have had to pull him out with a rod.

The once happy town, everybody greeting, being polite,
now they have to make things right!

The brown water smothering houses and escaping into
the cracks of doors, landslides on all of the moors.

The next day, watching families huddle together, looking
at their bare homes all because of this weather!

The new toys, the sobbing little boys, this is one
Christmas we'll never forget!

Kacey McWhir, Burnley Road Academy

I Was A Witness!

Bewildered, lost and distraught,
I stood there, staring at my beloved world...
Tears spilled from my sad eyes
I was unable, unable to speak, unable to smile,
Unable to help!

Through my blurred eyes,
I managed to make out my reflection in the cold, murky
water
My bloodshot eyes, my tearstained cheeks...
Me!

Ruined businesses, crushed buildings,
Destroyed homes!
As Mytholmroyd's Christmas finished early,
We struggled to escape the
Dreaded depressing feeling that echoed
From house to house, building to building!

Disease-infested sewage lingered
On the roads as people crowded like a swarm of bees!

Useless sandbags... Useless flood defences
Nothing saved us this time!

Rebecca Emily Sowden, Burnley Road Academy

Flood Poem

The fast flowing, filthy water grown along the emerald
garden. Like a swimming pool, the water covered the
road which is long gone. Why has this happened?
As the Land Rover swam in the water, it couldn't get up.
In the dirty water, you could see a reflection. Looking
down in the river, she thought, when will it stop? Why
has this happened? All the furniture was hanging high.
Why has this happened?
Why?

Riley Mcbride, Burnley Road Academy

The Boxing Day Floods

The path of the river quadrupled in size
The eternal depths of the river roared loud
During the floods of Boxing Day
The devastation was clear to see
Furniture felt decrepit and wretched
After the floods of Boxing Day
Emerald plants still holding up like a fort
The buildings were undersea mountains
During the floods of Boxing Day
The puddles reflected like mirrors
A junk pile eight metres high surveyed the wreckage
After the floods of Boxing Day
Water was furious, freezing and filthy

During the floods of Boxing Day
Remembering gushing, rushing and crushing water
After the floods of Boxing Day
A plethora of torrential rain subsided
During the floods of Boxing Day
Leaving a skeleton of the former town
After the floods of Boxing Day
The floods of Boxing Day.

Seth Thomas, Burnley Road Academy

The Mytholmroyd Flood

Laying there unwanted, unloved, unneeded, the rubbish
was deeply saddened.
Looking down feeling distraught the lady looked at the
devastated village.
Why here?
Yellow sandbags lay helpless against the tidal wave.
Floating in the filthy water the maroon Land Rover
nearly served as a deathbed for a poor old man.
Why here?
Debris lay there never to be used again.
Why here?
Why?

Joseph Brooke, Burnley Road Academy

Hopeful Hearts

The tall forts decreasing the chances of flooding,
clearing the clouds, enhancing the sun.
Someone smiling, someone crying.
People helping, people replying.
The barriers of hope
fixing the broke.

The smiles coming together makes people happier.
Please don't rain
 it's a shame,
 just smile like the volunteer
helping you clear,
just like a golden spear
helping a peer.

Amaad Hussain, Ryburn High School

Tears Before Laughter

As the morning starts,
the sound of dripping,
Too close for comfort.
To a sight of shock
And a hit to the heart.

The tears were falling.
Hearts were broken.
The minds were gone.
The road too flooded.
For cars to move.

As day ended,
The water still flowed.
But it started to low
And the clean-up crew started to go.

To salvage all they could.
Nothing was left!

As families started to build,
People do their best to group together
and the community joins them
singing and laughter is heard all around.

Alexander Houston, Ryburn High School

There's No Way Of Knowing

There's no way of knowing
We are flowing
Shops, buildings, homes, Lives are ruined
We're rushed into homes
By 4 x 4s
Who wants a swimming pool
In their front room?
Especially when there isn't much room
As furniture floats around too!
Cars aren't boats, yet Jeeps are?
What good does driving through a river do?
It pushes the water into the swimming pool
But yet what's now a swimming pool
Was once a home or two!

What kind of present on Boxing Day?
It must be awful, as someone has to pay.
Not a good start to a happy new year
The rush of the water
Rushed away all their good cheer
Basements are flooded, cars covered,
Water as high as a telephone line.
Home wash

But yet the water ,
What does the water think?
We will tower over buildings
Conquer like Henry VIII
We will knock down anything
If it stands in our way
We will rise, rivers and oceans
From their beds
We will have no rest
We will conquer
We will rise up
And be the king of the universe.

The spirits are fighting,
The community spirit.
The people say when sun is shining,
That's our silver lining.
Our tears no longer follow,
In time, we will re-grow.

What a sad show, full of tears, as
Memories flood right back at us,
And new ones, and new friends
Will live with us forever, we will
Remember all their love and trust, forever.

Liam Christie, Ryburn High School

Editor's note – one thing we all do when we're faced with bad times is to look back on when we were happy and remember to good times to keep us going. One contributor chose to do just that, thus making his own unique and poignant response to the flooding misery...

Manchester United

When Manchester United won the league in 2013, I was so happy when I saw the looks on the player's faces. It was such a pleasure to see my favourite team. I was so proud of Man Utd. Winning the league is a big thing in a football career. It was a magnificent goal from Robin Van Persie to secure the title.

Ryan Wadsworth, Ryburn High School